COFFEE & WILDFLOWERS

with love,
Abi ✱

COFFEE & WILDFLOWERS

ABI HAYES

First Edition 2022

ISBN: 978-1-3999-3734-4

for all of you I've sipped coffee
& shared stories with over a slice of cake

My grandmother was a mesmerising storyteller. Anyone who listened would hang on every note of her melodic voice. When I was little, she fed me tales of adventure, alongside a slice of freshly baked chocolate cake.

As I grew older, these stories became the answer to every question or concern life placed in my path; the remedies were always revealed between the lines. Granny Maggie knew which story I needed the moment she saw me. As we stood at her kitchen worktop, carefully weighing out ingredients, sieving the flour, and breaking the eggs, I would regale her with anecdotes of my week. She listened quietly, carefully, as the cake rose in the oven. It wasn't until that first slice was cut, and the tea was poured into her delicate blue teacups, that a story would trickle from her lips like honey and fill the room with its sticky sweet reassurance.

Now she's gone, and at first the silence was stifling. But when I listen closely, I can still hear her stories, like magic spells and poetic remedies whispering through the quiet.

This story is told with her magic words along with a few of mine, and I hope they help you feel held and heard in this unsteady world.

Love,

Hattie xo

Sit with me a while in my wildflower garden
whisper secrets among the cornflowers

Stir love spells into blossom honey fig cake
taste the golden nectar of reassurance
with every mouthful

Listen to the bittersweet words
brewed in your morning coffee
like a poetic remedy

when you lift the cup to your lips
make a toast to the ghosts of your past

& drink in all of the magic
the future has to offer

SNOWDROP
(GALANTHUS)

strength in the face of adversity

At 6.22 am, Hattie takes the final stairs onto the sleepy morning platform, the sound of her footsteps echoing through the underpass and her suitcase clanking up each step as she drags it behind her. Only a handful of commuters travel at this time; she embraces the emptiness of the station, unlike the occasional mornings when she's forced to take the 8.12. Those are the fateful mornings she finds her face thrust into sweaty armpits, or the top of her head sprinkled with the remnants of a sneeze. She's such an unfortunate height for busy commuter travel.

The winter sunshine is breaking through the trees beyond platform two, but she barely notices it, too busy glancing at the board for delays, her heart thudding at the decision she's made. She needs to be away by the time he reads the note she left on the breakfast bar.

She hears the announcement as the train approaches at 6.26 and makes her way to the same carriage she sits in every morning. She plants herself in the same seat, glances briefly at the same four suited commuters reading the Metro, earbuds in. Only today, she's not going to work, and she won't be making this commute again.

Hattie pulls down the little seat table, making space for her cappuccino and a slice of banana loaf, and removes her copy of the Metro from under her arm. As the train veers out of Putney Bridge, her body heaves a sigh of release.

She whispers goodbye to her beloved London—it will be hard to return after this. For one last time, Hattie looks into the windows of the same little houses that she rolls past every morning, admiring endless streets of identical brick terraces with gardens only big enough for a dustbin, and finally, her eyes fall on her own cosy house on the end with the red door. The house (and fiancé) she's leaving behind. Her heart starts to thud again as she thinks of the magnitude of her decision. The number of times she's tried to do this, and thought it impossible.

But now, thanks to her beloved Grandmother Maggie, she has somewhere to escape to and the strength she needs to go through with it.

* * *

SUNSHINE BANANA LOAF
(*Hattie's Escape Cake*)

Ingredients:

140g self raising flour
140g butter
70g caster sugar
70g soft brown sugar
100g chocolate chips
1tsp vanilla essence
2 ripe bananas, mashed
2 eggs

Method:

Preheat the oven to 180c. Grease and line a 2lb loaf tin.

Whisk together the butter, sugars, and vanilla essence.

Fold in the flour, eggs, banana, and chocolate chips.

Pour the mixture into a loaf tin and bake for approximately 50 minutes, or until a skewer comes out clean when inserted into the centre.

Remove from the oven and sprinkle on a few more chocolate chips, then place on a wire rack to cool.

Slice and enjoy with your morning cappuccino.

Luggage, train, exit sign

piece by piece
i've been preparing myself
for my great escape

at the back of my wardrobe
beneath coats and boxes of old books
somewhere i know you'll never look

sits my luggage, packed
ready to grab
when the time feels right

(sometimes i wonder if
it will ever feel right)
but what is it i'm waiting for?

you didn't come home last night
and i know that's my exit sign
i place the handwritten note

on the kitchen table
i put my hand on the cold metal handle
and heave the case from its hiding place

before i can change my mind
i look around our home one last time
    detached
        it's no longer mine

sometimes running is the bravest thing we can do
it's often the hardest path
and takes courage to realise
what isn't meant for you

don't look back

we were the first snowfall
of winter—
that luminous moment
in the forest
as the sun's rays
reach through the trees
igniting the beauty
of each icy leaf

but now we're the muddy
heaps
of salt, slush, grit
piled high
in abandon
at the side of the street

and all that remains
is the longing
for spring
to soar swiftly
through the biting air
& breathe warmth
to our skin

winter

in the end, i'm not sure if it was fear or intuition.

sometimes they sound the same, so maybe it was both—my inner choir in unison—telling me to run. so i listened to their chorus, surrendered to their voice, escaped the crescendo surrounding you, as i turned towards the door. you told me i'd regret it, but quite the opposite is true. i wish i'd done it sooner; i'm a sunflower in full bloom.

surrender and run

SUNFLOWER CHOCOLATE CAKE

Ingredients:

200g self raising flour
200g caster sugar
75g cocoa powder
450ml milk
2 tsp vanilla essence
2 ½ tbsp sunflower oil
icing sugar to dust

Method:

Preheat oven to 180c. Grease & line an 8" cake tin.

In a large mixing bowl, mix together the flour, cocoa powder & sugar.

In a separate bowl, mix the milk, oil and vanilla essence.

Pour the wet ingredients into the dry ingredients and mix together with a spoon.

Pour the cake mix into the cake tin and bake in the oven for 40-50 minutes.

Remove from the tin and cool on a wire rack.

Sprinkle with icing sugar and serve while warm.

in moments of hesitation, of indecision, do something that makes you feel still, that holds you safely, that brings comfort near

it can be difficult to hear your intuition over the sound of your fear

grounded

the greatest gift you gave me
was to walk away

the greatest gift I gave myself
was to let you

like a glass bauble on the tree
twinkling with fragility
in the fairy lights, you made me
afraid of heights
knowing that however gently
you could hold me
you could just as easily
drop me & watch me
f

   a

      l

         l
shatter into tiny pieces
as I hit the floor

and for a while I lay there,
broken
undeserving of being whole

until slowly, piece by piece,
I put together the shards
and realised that my cracks
were my most precious part
because those cracks are where
the light gets in

no longer living in the shadows
of the darkness that you cast

the greatest gift you gave me
was to walk away

the greatest gift I gave myself
was to let you

walk away

when you hear a whisper, a gentle voice inside your head, saying
i deserve better
listen to it.
how loud does your worth need to shout to be heard?

worthy

i spent too long gathering up
the crumbs of love
he left for me
unwanted on his plate

so i teach myself to bake

& soon my kitchen table
is lined with cake after cake
the kind with
buttercream frosting
rainbow sprinkles
a cherry on top
& he can see i'm not
starving anymore

he tells me i'll regret it
too much sugar will make me sick
says the crumbs should be enough for me

but i deserve the whole damn cake

accept nothing less

CHOCOLATE CUPCAKES
(the whole damn cake)

Ingredients

For the cake
170g butter
170g caster sugar
150g self raising flour
20g cocoa powder
3 eggs

For the frosting
260g icing sugar
140g butter
20g cocoa powder

Rainbow sprinkles and cherries to decorate

Method:

Preheat the oven to 180c and put cupcake cases in a muffin tin.

Mix together the butter & sugar until creamy.

Gently fold in the eggs, flour & cocoa powder.

Spoon mixture into cases.

Bake for 25 minutes, or until firm to the touch and a skewer comes out clean when inserted into the middle.

While the cakes are cooling on a wire rack, make the buttercream frosting by mixing all the icing ingredients together. If it's too thick, add a drop of milk.

Decorate the cupcakes with buttercream frosting, sprinkles and a cherry on top.

it's nothing you say or do
that breaks us
it's that you say and do
nothing to save us

your silence is heartbreak
aching to be heard
telling me it's over
without saying a word

half empty haiku

half empty teacup
you left on the breakfast bar
abandoned, like me

HAWTHORN

(CRATAEGUS)

where there is hope there is healing

Hattie wakes to the sound of seagulls scratching on the roof of her sunshine yellow campervan. She grumbles as she rolls over and looks at the time on her phone (far too early for a Sunday), noticing seven missed calls and three new voicemails. She doesn't need to listen to them to know they're from Josh, pleading for her return or, even worse, offering to move to St. Cloud's with her. Who knew it could be so heartbreaking being the heartbreaker? She tried; she really did try to make it work. She grimaces at the thought of him turning up in her haven, her favourite place. So she ignores the texts (including the ones from her mother), deletes the voicemails, and carries on living in a state of blissful avoidance.

Thirty minutes later, she's freshly showered and tussling with her wild curls, trying to tie them back with her sequined hair knot. She slides her feet into her flip flops, pulls on her honey bee sweater, unravels a fresh apron and pins her grandmother's bronze bee brooch to her sweater.

The brooch has become her favourite part of her uniform, always admired by her customers and evoking adoring memories of her grandmother.

Hattie steps out of the van's side door and opens the little hatch to reveal her shiny coffee machine, flipping the switch to hear it burr to life. As she pulls down the awning and unfolds the wooden tables and chairs to be ready for her first customers, she thinks how settled she feels here; it feels like home. For someone who has spent their life flitting from place to place, never really fitting in, this is particularly special. She has friends here, real friends like Rose, the kind you meet and instantly know they're going to be important to you. Rose would arrive shortly on her bicycle with fresh-cut wildflowers from her flower farm spilling from the basket and arrange them on Hattie's coffee tables. Hattie would return the favour with unlimited cappuccinos and sticky ginger cake (Rose's favourite).

The soft spring sun already feels warm on her red curls, and she breathes in the sunrise across St. Cloud's Bay. In front of her is a view across the entire bay, the sandy beach stretched out on either side of her, and the wooden boardwalk running the entire length of the village to the harbour on the far right. Behind her is the gravel drive where her little camper is parked, and a narrow paved path lined with lavender, iris, peonies, and lilacs that lead to her grandmother's dilapidated stone cottage. *Wildflower Cottage*, her new home.

Hattie has spent every waking minute (when she isn't baking cakes or frothing coffee) making the little cottage her home. At first she had been of two minds about changing anything at all, worried that it would erase her grandmother's memory, but she soon realised that changing the wallpaper wouldn't change the life they'd shared.

When she first walked through the front door, the jug of fresh-cut daffodils had still been blooming radiantly at the end of the dining table, beside half a loaf of sourdough bread sitting expectantly, waiting for Maggie to come home for another slice. Everything was exactly how she left it.

Hattie's eyes shone with the memories, heart aching. As Hattie looked around at her new home now—the faded yellow damask wallpaper, the armchair that needed upholstering, the kitchen that needed replacing—her eyes fell on the photo above the mantel of Maggie, Hattie, and her dad and everything else faded into the background. Maggie had never given up hope that, one day, Hattie's father would return, but that's where Hattie and Maggie had differed.

A few years ago, she went through a phase of seeing her dad everywhere she went. On the tube on her morning commute, in the supermarket in the bakery section—she'd even seen him on the Champs-Élysées in Paris once. But the truth was she wouldn't know if it was him anyway. Her last photo of him had been taken 25 years ago, and it was hanging here above the mantel in her new home.

The windows at the back of the house were the one saving grace of Hattie's new abode. There was a hint of magic in the air that poured through its panes and hovered like a halo, illuminating every inch of the house. And that view—that vast tumultuous ocean view—she could watch it all day long. Even on stormy days when the wind battered the harbour walls and the rain beat against her window panes, it soothed her to think it was all completely out of her control. And on a day like today, she could heave open those windows and fill the room with the lingering scent of Maggie's wildflowers, drifting in with the salty spring air.

As she stood at the window, she could make out a lone figure walking along the harbour wall towards the coffee van. Alfred was early this morning. She wouldn't open for anyone else at this time, but for him she would make an exception.

* * *

Alfred strides along the same route he's taken every morning for the past 36 years, except Christmas day and the morning Luke was born. His errand to collect the morning paper and coffee comes so naturally to him that he does it without thinking. His wife Isla loves doing the crossword while she has her marmalade toast and coffee. You'd think after all these years she would be able to complete a crossword with so much practice, but she always leaves Alfred one or two to do. They feel ready for their day when it's complete. Occasionally, if he doesn't know an answer (which is seldom, of course), she pretends not to notice him scouring their bookshelves for clues.

Coffee, he mutters to himself, *mustn't forget the coffees this morning. I never heard the end of it that time I thought instant would do. It was not up to the mark one bit; she still talks about it now. I really hope the coffee van's open this early, or I'm going to have to walk along to Rocky Point and try there.*

Success. Armed with two Americanos, a slice of lemon drizzle, pancakes and today's Herald, he heads back along the boardwalk feeling smug that he won't be getting a row.

The house is too quiet, he thinks as he unlocks the front door. Isla's voice isn't singing to him as he walks through the hall, the smell of warm toast isn't filling the air—just an empty painful silence.

He sits down with the paper and looks over at the chair where Isla used to sit waiting for him, pen in hand, eager for today's clues.

Would it always be like this? Would his chest always ache with emptiness?

He still takes that walk every morning. He doesn't know what else to do.

✳ ✳ ✳

Hattie follows Alfred along the coastal path. She worries about how absent he seems, like he's on autopilot going through the motions of life. Grief has a tendency to do that to a person—nothing matters anymore, just a vast lonely void where a loved one should be. She wants to make sure he arrives home safely, maybe do the crossword with him and keep him company for an hour until the cafe opens for the day.

As she stumbles on a pebble, Hattie's beloved brooch tumbles unnoticed onto the path and lies abandoned in the sand, golden wings shimmering in the morning sunlight.

✳ ✳ ✳

LEMON DRIZZLE
(Alfred & Isla's Favourite)

Ingredients:

225g butter
225g caster sugar
225g self raising flour
4 eggs
zest of half a lemon

For the drizzle
juice & zest of 1 lemon
3 tbsp caster sugar

Method:

Preheat the oven to 180c. Grease and line a 2lb loaf tin.

Mix together the butter & sugar until pale and creamy.

Fold in the eggs, flour & lemon zest.

Pour the mixture into the loaf tin and bake for approximately 50 mins.

While the cake is baking, make the drizzle by mixing together the lemon juice, zest & sugar.

Take the cake out of the oven and insert a skewer into the centre. If the skewer comes out clean, the cake is cooked all the way through.

While the cake is still warm, pour the drizzle over the top and sprinkle over a little extra sugar.

Remove the cake from the tin and leave to cool on a wire rack.

entire oceans
between us
but still
my heart is compelled
to you
my soul illuminates
at the thought
of you

you are everything
and nothing
all at once

the oceans between us

you were the sun in my sky and even now
somehow, your light still gives me
the strength to rise
and fall into the memories
of our sunlit conversations
where i forever find myself
lost in your illumination

in your orbit

written in the stars

we sit
your hand in mine
for days, weeks,
months at a time
not a single word
between us
but the quiet beauty
of our Love
resonating like an
old familiar song,
melodic in our bond

you don't know this place
can't find my face
but you know that i am Love
as you drift away
and that is enough for me

needs to be
enough for me

as your eyes grow wide
searching for safety
lost in long forgotten places
they fall on me
peacefully
your hand clings to mine
ceaselessly
i hold your fears steady

our memories treasured
float like feathers
on a breeze
leaving behind
another missing piece
of our story
another page blurring
ink smearing
words disappearing
line by line

as we sit
your hand in mine

and when it's time for you to go
and I think to myself
you've reached your final milestone
i realise
there is nothing final about you leaving
the memories, moments, stories that you're in
echo through our hearts
your milestones are part of our bones
part of who we are
and now

they're written in the stars

you were my
first home

my lighthouse

a harbour
for my soul
to stay

so is it
any wonder
that day after
day
          after
                    day

i still feel
a little bit

homesick?

ROSE'S STICKY GINGER LOAF

Ingredients:

225g self raising flour
175g butter
175g black treacle
175g muscovado sugar
1 tsp ground ginger
1 tsp mixed spice
200ml milk
2 eggs, beaten

Method:

Preheat oven to 180c. Grease and line a 2lb loaf tin.

Melt butter, sugar and treacle in a saucepan, then remove from heat and cool a little.

Stir in the milk and beaten eggs.

In a mixing bowl, sift together the flour and the spices.

Gently stir the wet ingredients into the dry ingredients, then pour into the loaf tin.

Bake for 50-55 minutes, then allow to cool completely in the tin.

Once removed and cool, wrap in baking paper and a tea-towel to keep moist.

yellow is
her favourite colour memory

the shade of her daughter's dress
when she took her first steps
silhouette stumbling unsteadily
against the soft spanish sunset

wildflowers in a jug
on the windowsill
coffee brewing
life holds still

lemon cake crumbs
on a china plate
sticky sweet drizzle
freshly baked

sunday mornings, newspaper spread
toasted soldiers dipped in the yolk of her egg
pancakes flipping
radio singing

and loving words
dripping like honey
on those zest filled
citrus days of summer

yellow is
her favourite colour memory

yellow

MAGGIE'S SUNDAY MORNING PANCAKES

Ingredients:

260g self raising flour
260ml milk
40g melted butter
100g caster sugar
2 eggs
½ tsp vanilla essence
oil/butter for the pan

Method:

Whisk together the eggs and milk.

Mix in the flour, sugar, vanilla essence and melted butter.

Heat a little oil in a frying pan, pour in 2 tablespoons of batter and cook for a minute or so until bubbles start to form on the surface of the pancake. Flip over, cook for another minute, then serve.

Hattie's favourite toppings are blueberries and whipped cream.

what felt like the end when i lost you
was the beginning of finding myself

recovery

Part 1: *Heartbroken*

it was winter when you left
but i think it might be time
for a spring clean,
to sweep away
the dirt and grit
that left me in bits

because i know i'm deserving
i know i'm worthy
of a fresh start

but as much as i can clean
what surrounds me
declutter my space
when i close my eyes
i can still see your face

if only i could spring
clean the memories
still haunting me

if only i could spring
clean my heart as easily
as the way you abandoned me

left me in a heap on the floor
without a second thought

i know it's time for
spring to soar in but
this season is long
and i still think of you

Part 2: *Heartbreaker*

it was winter when i left
this season is long
and i still think of you

out of the window i see
the trees shedding their leaves
letting go of the past
and i remember what we had
before i shed us too,
knowing it couldn't,
wouldn't last

is there a *good* way to leave?
is there a *nice* way to say
goodbye?

i tried, i promise you
i really tried

and i know you feel like
i abandoned you but i'd
abandoned myself long ago

staying
would have broken us both

so now i have only
memories haunting me
trees reminding me
of the love i let go

a winter of goodbyes
leads to a spring of what ifs
and a lifetime of the love
i wasn't able to give

it's time to forgive yourself
you did the best you could
with what you knew at the time

forgive yourself
you were just trying to survive

i'm sorry

you feel like you are broken. the cracks in your heart too deep and dark. too much damage to ever be enough. too heavy for the weightlessness of love. but there is someone who will hold your wounds gently. they will whisper words of comfort while serenading your scars. they will call your shattered fragments your most precious parts.

where the light gets in

to the wildflower
drifting in the wind

not allowing yourself to be tethered
by the gravity of connection

afraid of planting roots
afraid to *stay*

each time you settle on a steady surface
it slips away beneath you

so you circle high above
out of reach, far enough

& you decide that maybe love
is better from a distance

ode to a wildflower

LARKSPUR

(DELPHINIUM)

better days are coming

Exhausted, Hattie leans against the camper counter, feet aching. The golden hour of dusk illuminates her final remaining table of customers: an Italian family visiting her little Scottish seaside town. Hattie steals glances at them in the glass of the cake cabinet doors. *How is it even possible for one family to be so shiny and chic?* Hattie thinks as she catches her reflection, trying to tame her wisps of curls, but instead giving up and turning away.

She's still angry with herself for losing her grandmother's bee brooch; she hates how clumsy and careless she can be sometimes. Even the little girl, with chestnut hair and bright hazel eyes, seems to have her life more together than Hattie. She suppresses a yawn, and busies herself making their second (and hopefully final) round of espressos and slicing the honey fig cake. The family didn't even flinch when she turned the sign on the camper door to "closed," so she knew it was going to be a late one.

She finds the process of making the coffees a welcome distraction from her thoughts. She'd busied herself with fixing up Maggie's cottage, and catering for the first trickle of tourists of the season, as a way of avoiding Josh and her mother all together. However, she's beginning to think that maybe they were right and her move here had been a moment of madness, a romantic notion that was completely unrealistic. She's always been so good at leaving that she's not sure she even knows how to stay.

Hattie's phone buzzes in her apron pocket and she scrolls through her notifications absentmindedly. Her eyes widen as she reads the message, heart thumping.

Heard you're back in St. Cloud's—serving the best lemon drizzle in town according to my dad—maybe see you on my next visit. L

She shoves the phone back in her apron—now is not the time to complicate things (though her half smile suggests otherwise). She thinks of the last time they met at the art gallery where he was exhibiting. She'd planned to fade into the crowd, avoiding any awkward moments that might occur between them. But Luke had noticed her immediately and she knew everyone around them had sensed something—it was impossible not to feel the atmosphere illuminating between them. She'd left abruptly and hadn't spoken to him since.

A sweet, familiar scent draws her focus back to her customers and she looks down at the little girl who has appeared at her side.

"Rainbow Cookie," she sings in her melodic Italian accent.

"Sylvie, where are your manners?" her mother whispers over the gentle lull of the rippling waves.

"Rainbow Cookie, *please.*"

Hattie smiles at her. "Of course, I'll bring them right over." She watches the little girl toddle back to her table, open her backpack and pour out hundreds of colourful pieces of Lego, falling like little droplets of a rainbow onto the wooden table. Hattie sets the drinks down between the rainbow pieces, intrigued by what Sylvie is about to create.

As she walks away, the sweet, familiar scent she'd smelt earlier turns sour, rancid. She unties her apron (the little pocket bulging with pens, notepads, hair ties, crumbs) and rolls up the sleeves of her yellow sweater, lifting the back of her hand across her clammy forehead. It's marzipan—or, to her, the smell of manipulation.

She made marzipan with her mum when she was little. The two of them would stand together at the kitchen worktop—Hattie standing on a little wooden stool so she could reach. It was Hattie's job to add the almonds and roll the marzipan into little balls as her mother whispered words of love and light and sweet nothings into her ear; the kitchen sang with her adoring serenades. But there was no mention of the previous night, no apology, no remorse for when the alcohol brought the trauma to the surface and spat it out with venom, misdirected and landing on a little girl. When, like the many evenings before, a six year old lay stroking her mother's hair as she sobbed, telling her everything would be ok, and was told in return that it was her fault. It was all her fault. Gin and tonic nights rolled like thunder into marzipan mornings, over and over again until Hattie could no longer tell which she feared the most.

After her dad left when she was five years old, it was just Hattie and her mum (and her Granny Maggie whenever she was allowed to visit). Hattie had adored her father—they were inseparable for those early years, and to this day she had no idea why he left or what had happened to him. Her mum was never the same after he'd gone, and Hattie didn't blame her for the way she had treated her. She knew how hard her mum had struggled but as she grew older, she also knew that their relationship wasn't good for either of them. It was Hattie's grandmother who showed her that love didn't need to be fiercely intertwined with hurt. It was her grandmother who showed her her worth and to never forget the love that she deserved. And it was Luke who had been there for her throughout it all, his friendship never faltering. He knew every part of her and loved her anyway.

Hattie gazes over at the little girl with her Lego. Her nimble fingers flit from one tiny brick to the next, eyes darting to find the perfect piece. An entire world being created from nothing—a sorceress curating a magic kingdom. Just as Hattie is rebuilding her life. First the walls, then the turrets, then the drawbridge. Building and rebuilding, stronger and taller, solid, safe, protected. And a fortress door to firmly keep out the people who don't deserve her magic.

* * *

setting your boundaries is not a decision you make once, in a moment of strength and clarity. it's a decision you continue to make time and time again. during moments of vulnerability and fear, barriers feel even harder to maintain.

take a deep breath and remember why you needed them in the first place.

blurred edges

she listens to the murmurings
of her mind at midnight
memories that sting
like bees swarming, vibrating
chasing away her peace

be still she whispers
but the nightmares keep buzzing
the nectar dripping
sickeningly sweet

through the beating wings
of the swarm the clock ticks
on and the darkness drags her
along, tempting her with
the promise that dawn is coming

with its silent light
and taste of honey.

honey dawn

HONEYED FIG & ALMOND TART
(Summer in St. Cloud's)

Ingredients:

130g butter, softened
165g caster sugar
1 tablespoon grated lemon zest
1 tablespoon grated orange zest
1 teaspoon vanilla essence
3 eggs
180g ground almonds
75g plain flour
½ teaspoon baking powder
80g flaked almonds
6 figs quartered
90g honey

Method:

Pre-heat the oven to 180°C and grease a 28cm tart tin/pie dish.

Place the butter, sugar, lemon zest, orange zest and vanilla in a bowl and beat for 5-10 minutes, or until light and creamy.

Add the eggs, one at a time, beating well after each addition. Gently stir in the ground almonds, flour and baking powder. Then fold in the flaked almonds.

Spoon the mixture into the tin, and spread evenly. Place the figs into the almond mixture, pressing down slightly.

Bake for 45 minutes, or until golden. Remove from the oven and, while still hot, drizzle with honey.

live like a wildflower
grow your own way
don't be afraid
to take up
s p a c e

some people move to the city
in search of a life
to shout about
she moved to the city
to whisper into
a sea of quiet
anonymity
to be swallowed whole
by overbearing buildings
and roaring traffic
to hide among tree lined streets
paved with homes and lives
she could get lost in

in this city she is nobody
irrelevant
vanishing
into the crowd

in this city she learned
the art of disappearing
and lost the beauty
of being
seen

vanishing act

be like autumn

let go of the leaves
that feel too heavy

hold on to the roots
that keep you steady

don't be afraid to change
and grow

there's a strength that comes
from letting go

find beauty in the falling
as summer fades to autumn

AUTUMN CRUMBLE

Ingredients:

For the crumble topping:
    120g plain flour
    60g caster sugar
    60g butter, softened
For the fruit filling:
    300g cooking apples, diced
    30g brown sugar
    4 tbsp water
    115g blackberries
    ½ tsp ground cinnamon

Method:

Heat oven to 180C.

To make the crumble topping, place the flour, caster sugar and butter in a bowl and rub together to make crumbs.

To prepare the fruit, peel and dice the apples and place them in a baking dish with the blackberries. Sprinkle over the brown sugar and cinnamon, then spoon over the 4 tbsp of water.

Sprinkle the crumble mixture over the fruit and bake in the oven for 20 minutes or until the fruit is soft and the crumble is golden.

Serve warm with a spoonful of vanilla ice cream.

i keep hope close

but there are days
when suddenly
it feels so far away
like a sailing boat
drifting on a horizon
of turquoise waters
radiant in the distance
but painfully out of reach

i wait patiently
watching as it dreamily
ebbs through the waves
trusting in the current
beneath the surface
to bring it back
to shore

i watch you disappear
drift out to sea

do you know
that i'm a lighthouse?

your soul can
harbour safely
with me

friend ship

of all those we choose to live this life with
there is nothing quite like
the magic of

friendship

he knew she had to go
small towns were not safe
enough for hurt
as big as hers

she needed to heal
in a city of strangers

she didn't leave a note
she left an artist palette
a canvas, an easel
asking him to paint
a life for himself

and now, years later
his studio is filled with
brushstrokes that belong to her
memories etched in acrylics
sketched in charcoal
absorbed in watercolours
she is the essence of his (he)art

and if he can't be with her
at least he has this

he has this, at least
if nothing else

Luke

night at the art gallery

soft evening sunlight floods the art gallery
streaming through the arch windows
reaching across the wooden floorboards
casting a warm soothing glow

champagne glasses clink
amid the low murmur of admiring voices
the artist enters the room, receiving wide-eyed glances
he looks over at her; the air between them rejoices

she lets herself fall into the familiar feeling of him
holds her breath as he makes his way across the room
it's been so long since they last met and yet
now in this moment it feels like yesterday too

they don't need words; they feel it all
so rare are moments like these
standing there reflecting the timeless art
their love, the true masterpiece

something more

i've never found the words to tell you how i feel // all the fleeting moments lingering between what we are and what we could be//my stomach flips // the air between us shifts // our hearts lift // then fall back // into the gentle comfort of friendship.

RAINBOW COOKIES

Ingredients:

100g caster sugar
50g brown sugar
100g butter
180g flour
1 tsp vanilla essence
1 egg
2 bags of M&M's

Method:

Preheat the oven to 180c. Grease & line a cookie sheet.

Mix butter and sugars together in a bowl. Add the flour, egg, vanilla, and one bag of M&M's.

Scoop spoonfuls of dough onto the baking sheets and press 2 or 3 M&M's into each one.

Bake for 8-10 minutes, until golden around the edges but still soft in the middle. If you prefer crunchy cookies, bake them for a few minutes longer.

Leave on the baking sheet for 5 minutes then place on a wire rack. These are even more delicious when still warm.

that's the thing about building yourself a fortress—
knowing when it's safe to lower the
drawbridge and let people in

CORNFLOWER

(CENTAUREA CYANUS)

lean gently into love

Summer gently fades into Autumn in St. Cloud's, but the beach is still spilling with picnic blankets, striped umbrellas, and sandcastles, as sailing boats drift on the horizon. The garden of Wildflower Cottage is overrun with the last of the wisteria and honeysuckle, and, with lots of hard work and late nights, Hattie has finally moved out of the campervan and into her new home. The little yellow camper has become known as Wildflower Coffee and the holiday makers line up in anticipation each morning to be the first to get their hands on Hattie's cheese scones. The locals don't need to line up—Hattie makes a secret batch for them.

Alfred hasn't been to visit Wildflower Coffee for a few days now and Hattie is starting to worry; she knows he must be lonely since losing Isla. She's asked a few of the members of the elevenses coffee club, but they haven't seen him out along the coastal path, either. Just as she ponders whether to pay him a visit after the morning coffee rush, she sees him strolling along the harbour wall with a little boy whose wisps of white curls are falling into his eyes, his bright red wellies still damp from exploring rock pools.

At the other side of the little boy, holding his hand affectionately, is Luke. He has the same frame and gentle amble as Alfred. His hair is a darker shade of blonde now than when they were younger, but to her, he looks exactly the same as always. She feels a wave of guilt wash over her for having not replied to his message, for thinking that he could ever be complicated. The feelings are still there—the natural flow of their relationship and the instant connection they share every time they meet. There are some friendships that no matter how long passes, how far the distance, the connection stays the same; the hearts still align.

They sit down at Alfred's usual table nearest the beach, and Luke comes over to the counter. He greets her with a half smile, and she instantly relaxes into his soothing warmth.

"Alfred said to ask for his usual please." His voice is soft, with the hint of a west coast accent.

"Americano and a slice of lemon drizzle coming up," she replies with a smile.

"And I'll have a cappuccino, extra froth, extra hot and a hot chocolate with marshmallows for Alex, please."

* * *

Hattie gets to work on his order. She can feel his eyes on her, sensing that he wants to say something.

"Thank you for keeping an eye on Alfred," Luke says eventually, darting a glance at Hattie. He's never admitted it, but he's always wondered what would have happened if the timing had been right for them.

"Oh, it's nothing, really." She waves her hand dismissively. "He's lovely company and I know it can't have been easy recently—plus, I'm pretty good at a crossword challenge."

Luke laughs. "But still, you didn't need to, and I know it's meant a lot to him." He pauses, trying to figure out what to say next. "I didn't realise just how much he was struggling."

"Really, you don't need to explain. He does know how much you care," she reassures him, sensing the guilt he's been carrying.

"But I'll be around more from now on. I'm moving to the cottage on the corner with the blue door," he gestures over her left shoulder, a few doors down from Wildflower Cottage. "It has a space for my studio in the garden, and Alex can go to school in the village."

Hattie's eyes widen. "Oh that's great news...for Alfred, I mean," she mumbles.

Alex runs over to collect his hot chocolate. "Did you give her the brooch yet, Daddy?"

"Erm, oh yes, I forgot." He rustles around in his pocket while Hattie sneaks Alex a chocolate brownie and watches him carefully scurry back to Alfred.

"Alfred mentioned that you'd misplaced a brooch that was Maggie's, so I had a little look around St. Cloud's..."

"He's been looking every day for the past week," his father interrupts with a grin as he collects his americano and heads back to the table.

Luke clears his throat. "Well, just when I had a bit of spare time—it was nothing really. But this morning when I was walking along the coastal path, I found it." He hands her the brooch. "It's a little battered, but I polished it up and it's almost as new."

Hattie is lost for words. She smiles as she reaches for the brooch, her hand brushing his.

"Thank you," is all she can manage but he knows how much she means it. He leans in to her, pins the brooch to her apron. It was the moment they knew; this could be the start of something new.

Perhaps Wildflower Cottage hadn't been an escape—perhaps it was the place she could plant her roots, bury deep within the earth and let the soil of St. Cloud's nourish her soul. For the first time in her life, Hattie wanted to *stay*.

i stand on the shoreline
in the magic light of dusk
watching the gentle inhale
and exhale of the sea
after her storm
reminding me that she
too must take the rough
with the smooth
she too must surrender
to the stormy phase
and hold on for softer
waves to return

calmer days are coming
the sea told me so

she is ocean

deep beneath the crest
helpless shells swirling wildly
angry waves roll in

                              the final crest breaks
                          she rises from the seabed
                          breaks free of the storm

she was made of seaglass and treasures you find washed up on the shoreline after a storm. sharp edges softened and shaped by waves. a mosaic heart created of broken shards, carefully pieced back together.

whole again

let go of the past

take the love that was shown

& the lessons that helped you grow

but leave the weight behind you

so the light can find you

coffee with ghosts

she sits and drinks coffee
with the ghosts of her past
listening to voices
that haunt her
replaying conversations
thoughts in faraway places
all the things she should've done
all the places she could've gone
running from what she
thought she wanted

only to discover that all
roads lead back to
you

the sun's ruby hues
stretch across the bay
the morning light soothes
as they sit cocooned in
the start of something new

he breathes her in
cocoa and coffee beans
linger in the air
sea salt tangled
in her hair
from the ocean
this morning at sunrise

words stirred into
coffee cups
hearts wide open
past wounds shut

to him this is love
and he drinks it up

love brews

WILDFLOWER COFFEEVAN BROWNIES

Ingredients:

185g butter
185g milk or dark chocolate
275g caster sugar
85g plain flour
4 eggs
40g cocoa powder

Method:

Preheat the oven to 180c. Grease & line a 20cm square tin.

Melt the butter & chocolate in a bowl over a saucepan of simmering water, then set aside to cool a little.

In a separate bowl whisk together the sugar & eggs until frothy.

Stir in the melted chocolate mixture, then gently add the flour & cocoa powder.

Pour into the cake tin and bake for 30-35 minutes. You want it to be firm on top but still a little soft in the middle.

Take it out of the oven & leave it in the tin until it's cold, then cut it into squares & enjoy.

something I wish I had told you

you were born to experience an entire ocean of love but no one ever told you. instead you were left guessing, left questioning, your worth. discovering that love was fiercely intertwined with hurt.

but with me, you don't need to guess anymore. i will tell you everyday, just so you can be sure. with me you will know, without a doubt, with all certainty, how beautiful love can be.

you were born to experience an entire ocean of love and i hope you spend the rest of your life swimming in its sultry waters.

untethered

this year has left me standing in
          mid-air
untethered,
longing to feel the weight of
connection

higher and higher i rise
looking down on a world
unsteady on its feet,
balancing on the edge
of a virtual trapeze

and then i hear you calling

you,
the soft landing for my body to fall on

so i plant myself into the earth of you
bury deep within the roots of you

and in all this yearning
i'm finally learning
being grounded
doesn't need to mean

stuck

you say there's
so much uncertainty
but i say
listen closely, slowly
to the gentle inhale of
your precious breath
to the steady beat of
your wistful heart
stand at the water's edge
and you will know
with all that is sure
day
after
day
the tide will rise and fall

in the moments of
uncertainty
look to the things that stay
look to the waves as they
return each day
take my hand
& you will feel
(like the strength of
my love for you)

much is certain

much is true

listen & know

SCOTTISH SHORTBREAD ROUNDS

Ingredients:

150g plain flour
100g butter
50g caster sugar (plus extra for sprinkling)

Method:

Heat the oven to 180c. Grease and line a baking tray.

Put the flour, butter and sugar into a mixing bowl and combine the ingredients with your fingertips until it resembles breadcrumbs.

Bring the mixture together with your hands to form a dough.

On a lightly floured surface, roll out the dough to about 2cm thick.

Cut the dough into rounds and place on the baking tray. Sprinkle with the remaining caster sugar.

Chill the dough in the fridge for 30 minutes, then bake for 15-20 minutes until golden brown.

Leave on the tray to cool for 10 minutes.

as golden hues
of afternoon sunlight
stretch across ocean tides
pulling us dreamily
from one season to another

we begin anew

like the moon, the trees,
the tides, the sunrise, you & i;
there is magic in the change
in the growing
in evolving

always transforming
while parts of us stay

day after day
year after year
over and over

we begin anew

sunrise: the promise
that magic & hope shine bright
in the morning light

CEDAR COVE CHEESE SCONES

Ingredients:

225g self raising flour
60g butter
½ tsp salt
1 egg beaten, for the glaze
100ml milk
100g mature cheddar cheese, grated
1tsp baking powder

Method:

Preheat oven to 180c and grease & line a baking sheet.

In a large mixing bowl, rub together the butter, flour, baking powder and salt with your fingertips, then mix in 80g grated cheese.

Stir in milk a little at a time and bring together with your hands to form a dough.

Roll out the dough on a floured surface to about 3cm thickness, then cut into rounds.

Place on the baking tray, brush with beaten egg to glaze and sprinkle with grated cheese.

Bake in the oven for 10-15 minutes or until golden brown on top.

Serve warm with butter.

golden hour is

the starlit glow through the night

and the gentle promise

that with dawn

comes light

golden hour is

the colour of her love

now the colour of her grief

in her sundrenched memories

she learns how to live

golden hour

My Darling Hattie,

Wildflower Cottage was always our place, our home, our haven and now it's yours. I know you will make it your own with those you choose to call your family.

You and I are the most wonderful example that family is so much more than a bond of blood. I think deep down you've always known that I'm not your biological grandmother. We were brought into each other's lives by chance. Some may call it fate, but I call it perfect alignment.

I hope my stories have shown you that words of the heart are often left unspoken. Share your life with those who listen in the silence.

You deserve an entire ocean of love and I hope you spend the rest of your life bathing in its sultry waters.

Forever Yours,

Granny Maggie

coffee & wildflowers

do you remember when the sun shone high in the sky
the grass burnt yellow in the height of summer
crunching beneath our feet in the heat
the sprinkler working hard to nourish your plants
lilacs sighing with relief
wisteria swaying in the welcome breeze
and the soft scent of honeysuckle hovering between us

i watch as you lift your coffee cup to your lips
eyes closed, soul smiling
like a sunflower tilting its head towards the sun
you whisper to me there's no place you'd rather be

i sometimes worry that i've forgotten
the sound of your voice
but when i think of this day i hear it so clearly
sipping coffee in your garden with the wildflowers
feeling your heart and mine rejoice

THE END

EPILOGUE

Hattie smells the steaming hot cup of coffee on her bedside table before she even opens her eyes. She feels a hint of winter in the air as she sleepily gazes out of her bedroom window at the stormy ocean, brooding under a heavy grey sky. In the cosy refuge of Wildflower Cottage, she pulls her granny's cable knit blanket around her shoulders and wraps her hands around her coffee cup.

Luke and Alex's hushed voices drift up the stairs from the kitchen, along with the familiar clattering of whisks and pans, reminding her that Sunday mornings are for coffee and pancakes with her family. She holds these moments still and steady—no more running away, she has learned how to *stay*.

Hattie lifts the cup to her lips, makes a toast to her Granny Maggie and drinks in all of the magic this moment has to offer.

RECIPE INDEX

BAKING CONVERSIONS

1 cup flour = 115 grams

1 cup caster sugar = 200 grams

1 cup brown sugar = 200 grams

1 cup icing sugar = 120 grams

1 cup cocoa powder = 85 grams

1 cup butter = 230 grams or 2 sticks

1 cup chocolate chips = 180 grams

1 tbsp honey = 21 grams

1 cup milk = 240ml / 227 grams / 8 ounces

1 cup grated cheese = 100 grams

measurements taken from www.sallysbakingaddiction.com

ACKNOWLEDGEMENTS

Calum, Cameron & Lucy-Rose: thank you for showing me everyday that love is infinite. For the patience and space you have given me to write this book, and for believing in me every step of the way. You are my forever.

To my beta readers: your encouragement and honesty while this book was in creation meant the world to me- thank you.

To my editor B. Laux: for holding my collection gently in its vulnerability and making me believe that this could actually be possible!

To my mentor and proofreader Shelby Leigh: this would still be a bunch of poems in my notes app if it weren't for you- thank you.

To Esther Emily Designs: for your beautiful illustrations that gave vision to my words.

To my readers: I hope this book makes you feel held and heard in this unsteady world. Thank you for choosing my book.

My family and chosen family: for all the summer afternoons spent sitting among the wildflowers sipping freshly brewed coffee with a slice of cake, talking about everything and nothing. So thankful for the poetic moments we share.

To my writing family: The Poetry Club members and the Thursday Night Creative Writers- this book would not be here without your compassion and encouragement. Forever thankful for you.

And finally, to friendship: the sunshine that fills my soul.

ABOUT THE AUTHOR

Abi is a poet, baker and coffee drinker living on the east coast of Scotland. Her poetry has been published in magazines and anthologies as well as performed at spoken word events. Coffee & Wildflowers is Abi's first book but she has many more poems stored in the notes app on her phone that may make it on to the page someday. When she isn't baking or writing, you'll find her at the beach with her husband, children and mischievous puppy.

Printed in Great Britain
by Amazon

16451145R00068